You Can Draw

Boats

Gareth Stevens
Publishing

Please visit our website, **www.garethstevens.com**.
For a free color catalog of all our high-quality books,
call toll free 1-800-542-2595 or fax 1-877-542-2596.

Library of Congress Cataloging-in-Publication Data

Bergin, Mark, 1961-
Boats / Mark Bergin.
     pages cm - (You can draw)
Includes index.
ISBN 978-1-4339-7466-3 (pbk.)
ISBN 978-1-4339-7467-0 (6-pack)
ISBN 978-1-4339-7465-6 (library binding)
1. Boats and boating in art-Juvenile literature. 2.
Drawing-Technique-Juvenile literature. I. Title.
NC825.B6B47 2012
743'.8962382-dc23
                              2011052970

First Edition

Published in 2013 by
Gareth Stevens Publishing
111 East 14th Street, Suite 349
New York, NY 10003

© 2013 The Salariya Book Company Ltd

Editor: Rob Walker

Printed in China

CPSIA compliance information: Batch #SS12GS: For further information contact Gareth Stevens,
New York, New York at 1-800-542-2595.

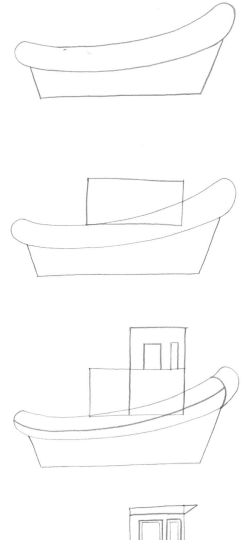

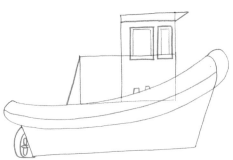

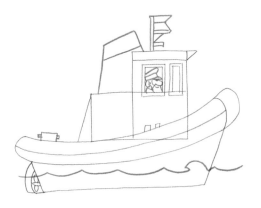

You Can Draw

Boats

By Mark Bergin

Contents

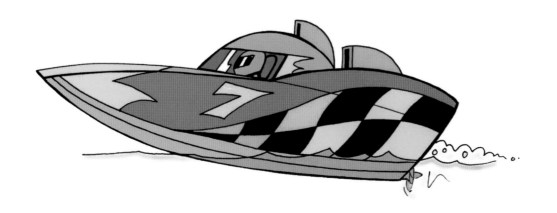

Introduction

Learning to draw is fun. In this book, a finished drawing will be broken up into stages as a guide to completing your own drawing. However, this is only the beginning. The more you practice, the better you will draw. Have fun coming up with cool designs, adding more incredible details, and using new materials to achieve different effects!

This is an example showing how each drawing will be built up in easy stages. New sections of drawing will be shown in color to make each additional step clear.

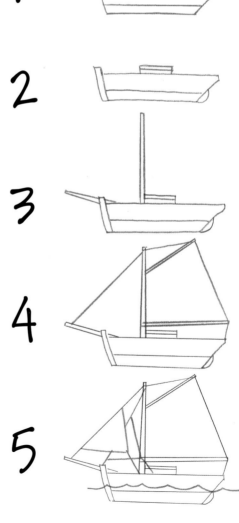

1

2

3

4

5

With practice, you too will be able to draw boats just like the examples shown here.

Materials

There are many different art materials available that you can use to draw and color your boats. Try out each one for new and exciting results. The more you practice with them, the better your drawing skills will get!

Use a pencil to draw the shape of your boat. Any mistakes you make can easily be erased, as can any construction lines that are left over at the end of your drawing.

An eraser can be used to rub out any pencil mistakes. It can also be used to create highlights on pencil drawings.

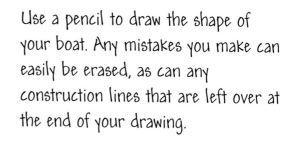

You can go over your finished pencil lines with pen to make the lines bolder. But remember, a pen line is permanent, so you can't erase any mistakes!

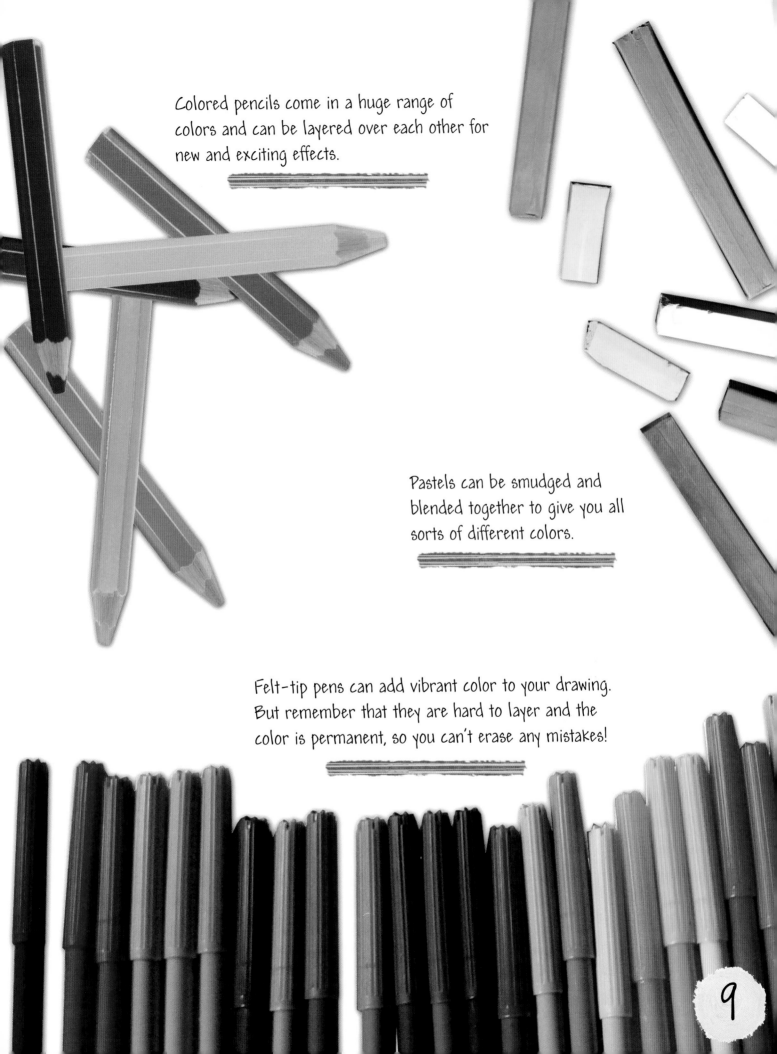

Colored pencils come in a huge range of colors and can be layered over each other for new and exciting effects.

Pastels can be smudged and blended together to give you all sorts of different colors.

Felt-tip pens can add vibrant color to your drawing. But remember that they are hard to layer and the color is permanent, so you can't erase any mistakes!

Inspiration

Many types of boats are made throughout the world. You can choose any of them as the inspiration for your cartoon-style drawing. Looking at photos, magazines, or books can give you new ideas and new designs to try.

When turning your boat into a cartoon-style, two-dimensional drawing, concentrate on the key elements you want to include and the overall shape of the boat.

One way to make your boat look cool is to exaggerate its key features and perhaps add new ones!

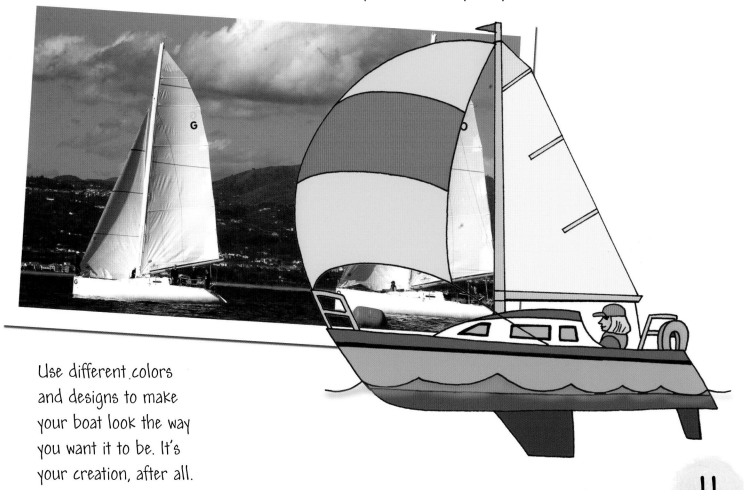

Use different colors and designs to make your boat look the way you want it to be. It's your creation, after all.

Laser

The Laser dinghy is a small sailing boat usually piloted by one person. It is used for leisure and racing, and in 1996, it became an Olympic-class boat.

Start by drawing the shape of the hull. Draw a line through it.

Add another line higher up and draw in the centerboard.

Draw the mast using curved lines, and then add the shape of the sail.

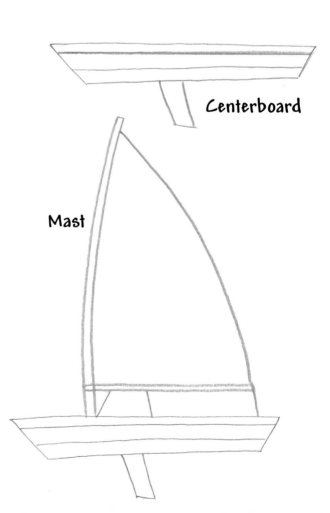

Centerboard

Mast

Add more detail to the sail
and draw in the rudder.

Rudder

Draw the sailor and
some waves for the
waterline.

Complete any final details,
then add color to the sail
and boat. Remember to add
color to the water the boat
is sailing in.

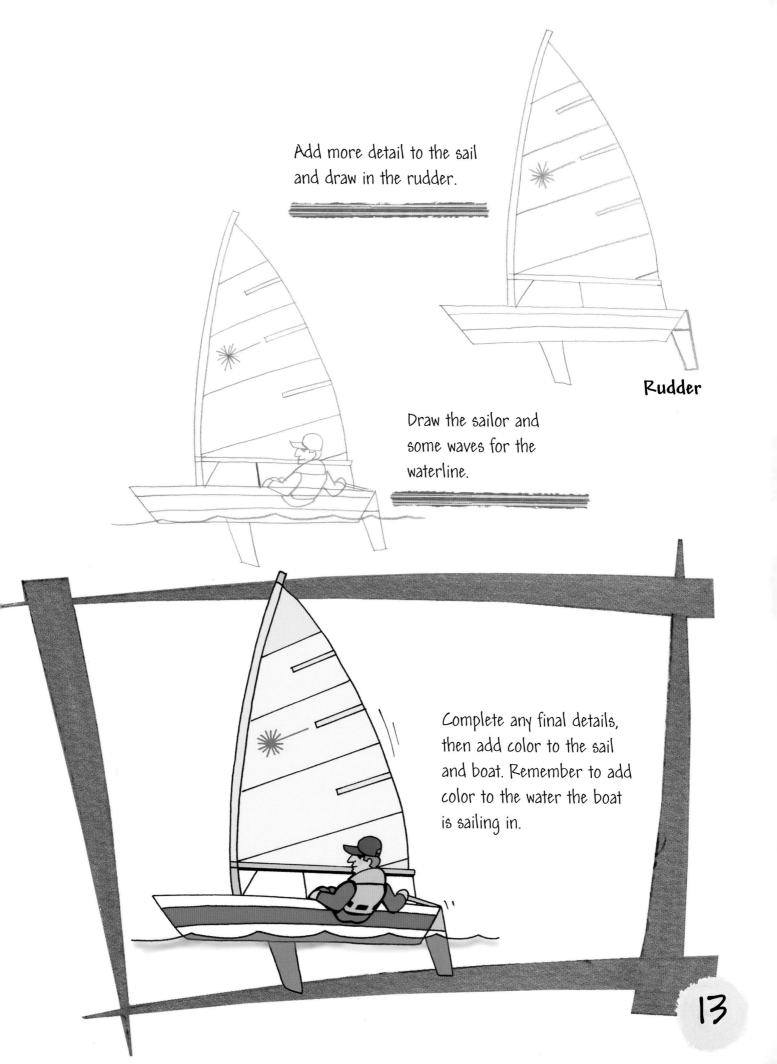

13

Racing boat

These high-performance racing boats are specially designed to move across the water at high speeds and take part in very exciting races.

Start by drawing the shape of the hull.

Extend the hull at the rear. Add a line along the top of the hull.

Draw a curved line on the underside of the hull. Add the small, domed cockpit.

Engine intakes

Add another curved line to the base of the hull and a window to the cockpit. Draw the large engine air intakes.

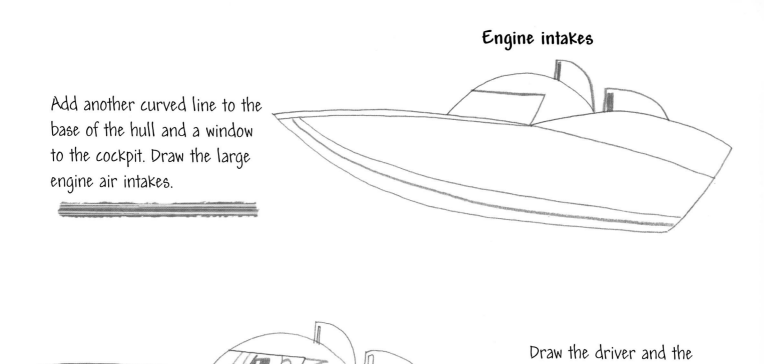

Draw the driver and the paintwork designs. Add the wavy waterline and a propeller.

Propeller

Complete all the remaining details and add color to your drawing. Remember everything below the waterline should be colored blue!

US coast guard

The coast guard boat has to be fast and durable in all weather conditions to mount rescues and police the shores.

Start by drawing the shape of the hull.

Draw the cabin shape rising above the hull.

Bridge

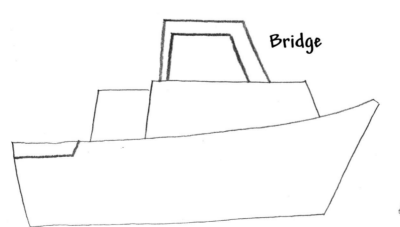

Draw the bridge with a window. Add extra detail at the rear of the hull.

Draw a propeller. Add the paintwork design and more detail on the window.

Propeller

Radar

Light

Add the pilot and draw an antenna, radar, and light. Add more detail to the cabin. Draw the waterline.

47

Complete your drawing by finishing any remaining details and then color the different sections of the boat.

Powerboat

This powerboat can be used out at sea for pleasure cruises or even for sports like fishing or diving.

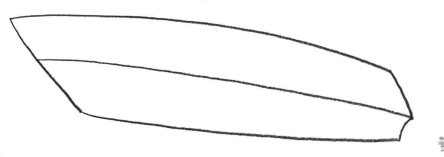

Start by drawing the shape of the hull. Add a line through the middle.

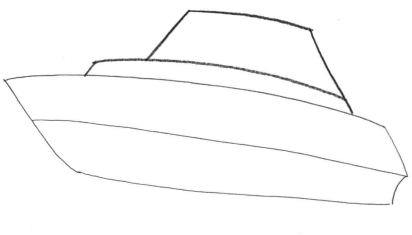

Add the cabin shape and the bridge.

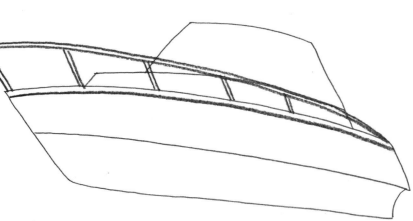

Add a railing on top of the hull.

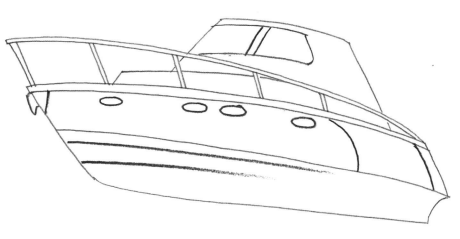

Draw a window in the bridge and portholes around the hull. Add two lines on the lower part of the hull.

Radar

Draw the pilot and the radar. Add the waterline and a propeller.

Complete your drawing by adding any remaining detail, then color it.

RHIB

A rigid-hulled inflatable boat (RHIB) is a lightweight boat that is designed to adapt to all weather conditions.

Start by drawing the two sections of the hull.

Draw the control panel and window.

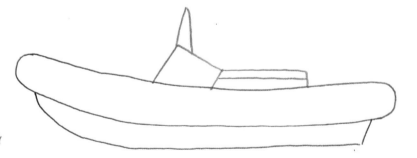

Draw the ropes along the top section of the hull. Add an outboard motor at the rear.

Outboard motor

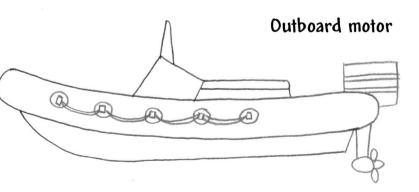

Draw a line through the lower part of the hull and add some small details. Draw the framework at the rear of the boat and add an antenna and radar.

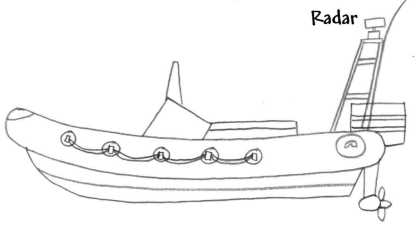

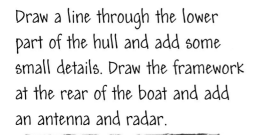

Draw the pilot at the controls and add the waterline.

Complete all the remaining details, then color the different sections of the boat.

Sailing boat

This classic sailing boat harnesses the power of the wind in its sails to propel it forward.

Start by drawing the shape of the hull.

Add the cabin shape.

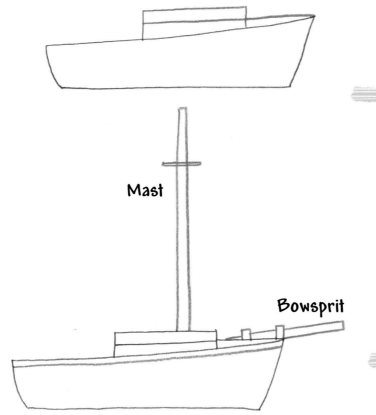

Mast

Bowsprit

Draw the mast and the bowsprit. Add a curved line along the top of the hull.

Add two lines between the
mast and the bowsprit.
Then draw the boom and
add the sails.

Boom

Add the pilot, a rudder,
and the cabin portholes.
Draw the waterline.

Finish off your drawing by
coloring it and adding any
small design details.

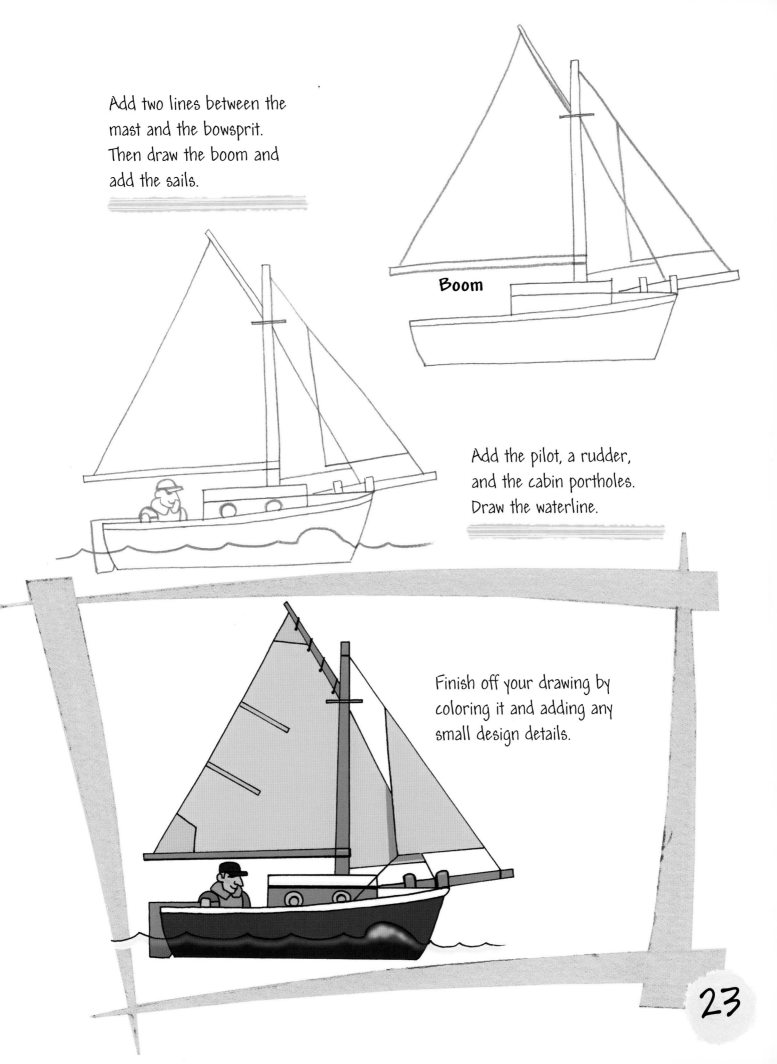

Tugboat

A tugboat is a small, powerful vessel that is used to guide bigger boats in and out of harbors by towing or pushing them.

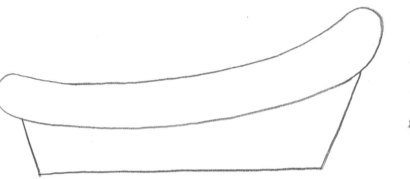

Start by drawing the two sections of the hull.

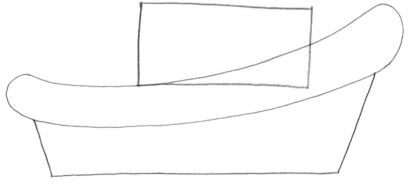

Add a rectangle for the main structure of the boat.

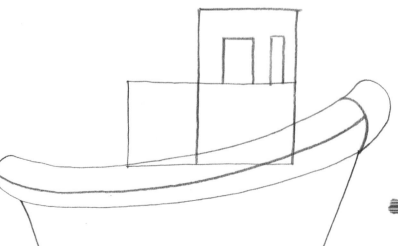

Draw an upright rectangle for the bridge and add windows. Add detail to the top part of the hull.

Draw the roof and windows of
the bridge. Add some details
to the main structure and draw
a propeller.

Radar

Funnel

Draw a funnel and add the
radar structure. Add the pilot
and the extra detail at the
rear. Draw the waterline.

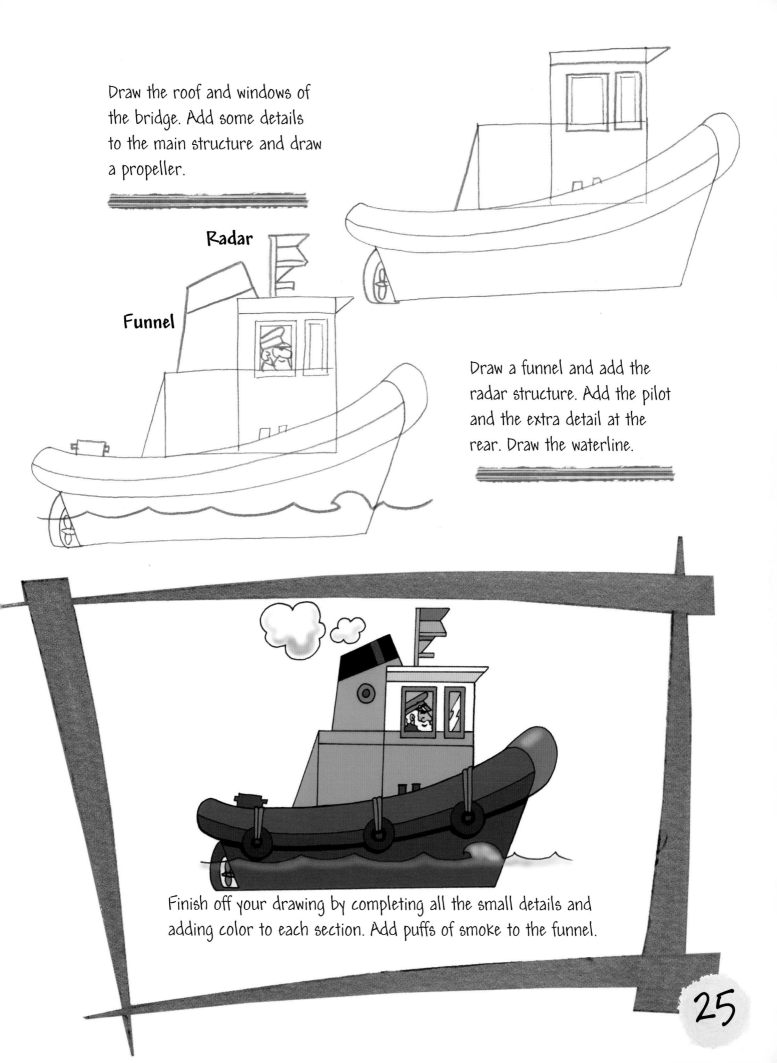

Finish off your drawing by completing all the small details and
adding color to each section. Add puffs of smoke to the funnel.

Fishing boat

This boat is used for the sport of ocean fishing. The rods at the rear are used to try to catch large fish or even sharks!

Start by drawing the shape of the hull.

Draw the cabin and bridge above it.

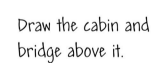

Draw a front railing and add a window to the cabin. Add a line to the hull.

Draw the small details near the bow and the waterline. Add a propeller and rear platform.

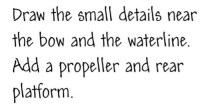

Bow

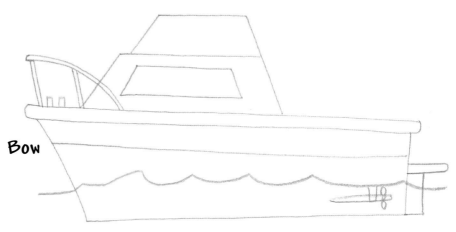

Propeller

Draw a large X-shaped frame with a roof. Add the pilot and three fishing rods.

Complete your drawing by adding all the remaining details and coloring it.

27

Yacht

This yacht can be used purely for pleasure sailing or for small journeys.

Start by drawing the shape of the hull. Add a line along the top edge.

Draw the cabin and add another line to the hull. Draw the fin keel underneath the hull.

Fin keel

Mast

Draw the mast and the rudder.

Rudder

Draw railings at the bow and stern. Add the boom to the mast and draw the sails. Add windows to the cabin.

Boom

Add a billowing sail at the bow and draw the pilot. Add the waterline.

Color the different sections of your yacht. Add any extra design details you wish.

More views

For an extra challenge, try drawing your boats from the front or rear! Practicing different views will help you improve your drawing.

Front View

Start with the hull of the boat.

Add the main structure and the waterline.

Draw the mast and a sail.

Draw another sail and a window.

Yacht

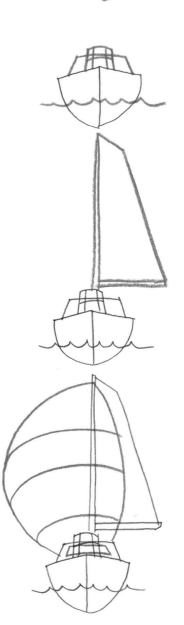

Back View

Tugboat

Start by drawing the shape of the hull.

Draw the main structure. Add propellers and a rudder to the hull.

Add the bridge and draw the waterline.

Draw windows, antennas, a door, and a radar. Add the side rails and two dots above the waterline.

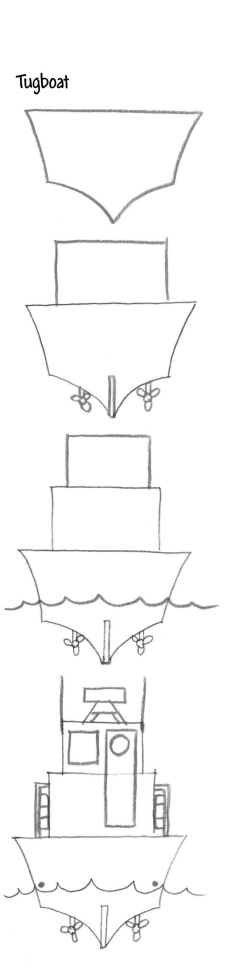

Glossary

boom A long pole used especially to stretch the bottom of a sail.

bow The front of a boat or ship.

bowsprit A large pole for sails sticking out from the bow of a ship.

cockpit An open space in the deck from which a small boat is steered.

dinghy A small rowboat or sailboat; especially one carried on a larger boat.

hull The main body of a boat or ship.

keel A timber or plate running lengthwise along the center of the bottom of a boat and usually sticking out from the bottom.

mast A long pole that rises from the bottom of a ship or boat and supports the sails.

rudder The hinged flap at the stern of a boat that is used to steer it.

sail A sheet of fabric used to catch wind to move a craft through water or over ice.

stern The rear of a boat or ship.

Index